The DADGAD Gospel

Gospel Guitar Solos in DADGAD Tuning

El McMeen & Sandy Shalk

Online Audio

D1223640

To access the online audio go to:
WWW.MELBAY.COM/30862MEB

The Brazilian Rosewood OM with Curly Redwood Top is courtesy of Franklin Guitar Company.
Photo by Notley Hawkins.

Exclusive Sales Agent: Mel Bay Publications, Inc.
WWW.MELBAY.COM

Contents

Title	Page	Audio

Preface

The great guitar tuning DADGAD, invented by the late British guitarist David ("Davey") Graham in the mid-20th Century, has provided the canvas for a variety of musical renderings in different genres. Mr. Graham himself played originals, Celtic music, jazz, middle-Eastern music, and other types of music in the tuning. It has been a mainstay of fingerstyle players around the world who have been exploring its endless possibilities.

Sandy Shalk, one of the authors of this book, has presented two lengthy DVD lessons of jazz and traditional music in DADGAD for Stefan Grossman's Guitar Workshop and Mel Bay Publications. Those lessons are entitled "Fingerstyle Guitar in DADGAD" and "Further Adventures in DADGAD." El McMeen has arranged many different types of music in various tunings, and has recorded DVD's for Stefan Grossman's Guitar Workshop and written books for Mel Bay Publications.

This folio focuses on the authors' arrangements of gospel music in DADGAD. It features some wonderful music that may be "below the radar" for fingerstyle guitar players but is well-known among gospel singing groups and their audiences. The level is generally for advanced beginner/intermediate players. That having been said, players may encounter some challenges in certain tunes if not familiar with the alternating-bass/"thumb-style" picking. Moreover, some of the arrangements have rich chordal support for the melody, and a player looking to simplify need only leave out some of the middle voices in the chords. Just be sure not to lose the melody in that approach.

We hope you enjoy playing this music as much as we enjoyed arranging it. Feel free to listen to sung versions of the tunes on the Internet to hear the phrasing and rhythms. That's what we did!

Best regards,

El and Sandy
NJ and Delaware

Blessed Assurance

Phoebe Palmer Knapp
Arr. Sandy Shalk

This page has been left blank to avoid an awkward page turn.

Down in the River to Pray

Down in the River to Pray (Page 2/3)

9

This page has been left blank to avoid an awkward page turn.

Drifting Too Far from the Shore

Holy Manna

Wm. B. Bradbury
Arr. Ellsworth McMeen

(Evoking a Salvation Army Band)

Holy Manna (Page 2/2)

15

In Christ There is No East or West

In the Great Triumphant Morning

Robert Emmett Winset
Arr. Ellsworth McMeen

Just As I Am

William B. Bradbury; Charlotte Elliott
Arr. Ellsworth McMeen
(Thanks to Gene Zasadinski)

20

Must Jesus Bear the Cross Alone?

Must Jesus Bear the Cross Alone? (Page 2/2)

23

On Jordan's Stormy Banks

This page has been left blank to avoid an awkward page turn.

Softly and Tenderly

Will L. Thompson
Arr. Sandy Shalk

This page has been left blank to avoid an awkward page turn.

The Hallelujah Side

Johnson Oatman, Jr.
Arr. Ellsworth McMeen

There Is Power in the Blood

Lewis E. Jones
Arr. Ellsworth McMeen

What a Friend We Have in Jesus

Charles C. Converse
Arr. Ellsworth McMeen

When I Can Read My Title Clear

J. C. Lowry; Isaac Watts
Arr. Sandy Shalk

Whiter Than Snow

William G. Fischer
Arr. Sandy Shalk

Will the Circle Be Unbroken

Yes, I Know

Anna W. Waterman
Arr. Sandy Shalk

El McMeen   Sandy Shalk

Psalm 150

(King James Version)

¹Praise ye the LORD. Praise God in his sanctuary: praise him in the firmament of his power.

² Praise him for his mighty acts: praise him according to his excellent greatness.

³ Praise him with the sound of the trumpet: praise him with the psaltery and harp.

⁴ Praise him with the timbrel and dance: praise him with stringed instruments and organs.

⁵ Praise him upon the loud cymbals: praise him upon the high sounding cymbals.

⁶ Let every thing that hath breath praise the LORD. Praise ye the LORD.

Manufactured by Amazon.ca
Bolton, ON

25662889R00028